THE PHILOSOPHER'S NOTEBOOK

to accompany

The Philosopher's Way
Thinking Critically About Profound Ideas

JOHN CHAFFEE
CITY UNIVERSITY OF NEW YORK

PEARSON

Prentice
Hall

Upper Saddle River, New Jersey 07458

© 2005 by PEARSON EDUCATION, INC.
Upper Saddle River, New Jersey 07458

ISBN 0-13-152428-3

Printed in the United States of America

Preface

This notebook, *The Philosopher's Notebook*, contains several of the *Think Critically* and *Think Philosophically* critical thinking activity boxes found in your textbook, *The Philosopher's Way*, by John Chaffee. This notebook is designed to serve as a journal where you can inscribe your thoughts and ideas as you think and meditate on the various questions in these critical thinking activities. Of course, a notebook such as this cannot contain enough pages for you to author a complete journal! The pages have been perforated so you can easily remove them and add them to your own journal, *YOUR Philosopher's Notebook*.

My Philosophy of Life

Everybody has a philosophy of life. Identify some of the foundation beliefs that form your philosophy of life, using these questions as a guide. Express your ideas as completely and clearly as you can. Encourage yourself to think deeply and beyond superficialities, to refuse to be satisfied with the first idea that you have, to move to deeper levels.

- What do you most value in life? Why?
- What moral beliefs influence your choices and your behavior toward others? How do you determine the "right" thing to do?
- What role do religious beliefs play in your life? Do you believe in "God"? Why or why not? Is there an afterlife? What is the path to it?
- What gives your life meaning? What is the purpose of your life? What do you hope to achieve in your life?
- How do we find truth? How do you know when you "know" something is true? What is an example of something you know to be true?
- Do you believe that your choices are free? Do you hold yourself responsible for your choices?
- What do you consider to be "beautiful"? Why? What is the function of art? Should "extreme" forms of artistic expression be censored? Why or why not?
- Are all people entitled to basic human rights? Why? What is justice?
- What are other important beliefs in your life?

_____

_____

_____

_____

_____

_____

_____

_____

_____

_____

_____

_____

THINK CRITICALLY

Who Is a Critical Thinker?

Think about people you know whom you admire as expert thinkers and list some of the qualities these people exhibit that you believe qualify them as "critical thinkers." For each critical thinking quality, write down a brief example involving the person. Identifying such people helps us visualize the kind of people we'd like to emulate. As you think your way through this book, you will be creating a *portrait* of the kind of critical thinker you are striving to become, a *blueprint* you can use to direct your development and chart your progress.

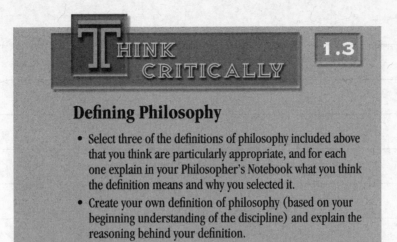

THINK CRITICALLY

1.3

Defining Philosophy

• Select three of the definitions of philosophy included above that you think are particularly appropriate, and for each one explain in your Philosopher's Notebook what you think the definition means and why you selected it.

• Create your own definition of philosophy (based on your beginning understanding of the discipline) and explain the reasoning behind your definition.

THINK PHILOSOPHICALLY

1.5

What Is Reality?

What is your idea of "reality" and where does it come from? Reflect on your daily media consumption—the hours you spend with a television, a magazine, or online. Do you question what you are viewing, critically evaluating the content and interpretations that are being presented? Or is it easier to simply absorb what you are viewing and hearing without intellectual probing and analysis? Describe one aspect of your view of what's "real" that has likely been influenced by the bias of your source of information. For example, what are your views on other countries in the world and the people who inhabit them?

_____

_____

_____

_____

_____

_____

_____

_____

_____

_____

_____

_____

_____

_____

_____

_____

_____

_____

_____

THINK PHILOSOPHICALLY

Am I Free?

1.6

Reflect on some of the limitations to your freedom. Are you locked into situations that present limited opportunities? Have you actively considered making different choices to change those circumstances? Are you passively content to choose from a limited selection of alternatives that are presented to you, instead of using your imagination to create a wide range of possibilities? Is your life limited by self-imposed constraints that result in unsatisfying or destructive choices? Have you explored strategies for removing these constraints so that you can make genuinely free choices?

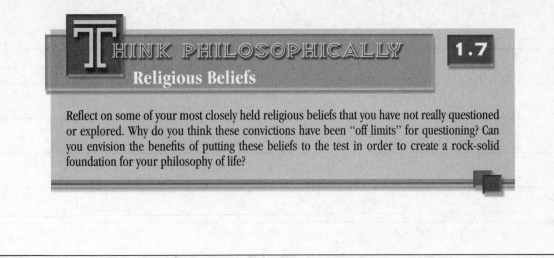

THINK PHILOSOPHICALLY 1.7

Religious Beliefs

Reflect on some of your most closely held religious beliefs that you have not really questioned or explored. Why do you think these convictions have been "off limits" for questioning? Can you envision the benefits of putting these beliefs to the test in order to create a rock-solid foundation for your philosophy of life?

THINK PHILOSOPHICALLY

Constructing Knowledge

1.8

Reflect on your approach to the information you receive from the sources in your life: friends, family, teachers, books, television, newspapers, the Internet, magazines, and so on. How often do you make a special effort to question, analyze, and critically evaluate the information? How often do you tend to simply accept the information in the form it's provided? In what ways would taking a more critical thinking approach to information help you construct well-supported knowledge?

THINK PHILOSOPHICALLY 1.10
Making Moral Decisions

Think about some of the particularly confusing and challenging moral decisions that you've had to make in your life. What made these decisions so difficult? Do you believe that you have a clear and accurate moral compass that you can use to guide you when complicated moral dilemmas arise in the future? What are some of the moral areas of your life in which you would like to have a clearer set of values?

_____

_____

_____

_____

_____

_____

_____

_____

_____

_____

_____

_____

_____

_____

_____

_____

_____

This course in philosophy is going to provide you with a unique opportunity to respond to Socrates' challenge by exploring profound ideas, developing powerful intellectual abilities, and developing as a reflective, insightful thinker. This first chapter has provided you with an introduction to the grand subject of philosophy and is also designed to be a personal invitation for you to begin—or continue—your own personal philosophical journey. Think about the philosophical themes and ideas that you have examined in this chapter, and then write a three-plus-page paper for your Philosopher's Notebook that explains your personal goals for this Introduction to Philosophy course. Discuss the insights you would like to achieve, the ways you would like to develop your mind, the knowledge you would like to achieve.

THINK PHILOSOPHICALLY
Archetypal Figures

2.1

Who are some of the influential thinkers and creative artists who have influenced your own intellectual development through exposure to their ideas and creations? After you identify one or two such figures, provide examples of the impact their ideas or lives have had on your own personal, intellectual, or creative development.

_____

_____

_____

_____

_____

_____

_____

_____

_____

_____

_____

_____

_____

_____

_____

_____

_____

Imagine that walking down the street you encountered Socrates, who engaged you in the following exchange:

Socrates: Tell me, did you go to philosophy class this week?

You: Yes, twice.

Socrates: And did your professor mention the philosophical challenge to "Know thyself"?

You: Yes, my professor did.

Socrates: And did you take no thought of that inscription, or did you attend to it, and try to examine yourself, and ascertain what sort of character you are?

You: (Complete your response in your Philosopher's Notebook.)

In your Philosophy Notebook, think philosophically regarding Socrates' response to the oracle by responding to the following questions:

- How do you think most people would respond to being told that they are the most intelligent person in their community? Why do you think Socrates reacts as he does?

- In another part of the *Apology*, Socrates explains how he interviewed people who were exceptionally talented in one particular area, such as poetry or the arts. He found that these people believed that "because of their poetry (or other talent), they thought that they were the wisest of men in other matters too, which they were not." Describe several examples of people you know who are talented in one area and who believe that they are exceptionally wise in other areas as well.

- Socrates freely admits that after exposing the errors and ignorance of supposedly "wise" people, they were "indignant." This may be something of an understatement, as according to an eyewitness account by Diogenes Laertius, Socrates frequently provoked opponents to attack him with their fists and tear his hair out, "yet he bore all this ill-usage patiently." Why do you think some people had such negative reactions to Socrates' rational inquiries?

- As we noted, Socrates is a very complex individual. Do you think that he really believes that he is only a "little wiser" than others, and that his advantage is solely due to his acceptance of the fact that he is *not* wise? Why or why not? Why is the admission of ignorance the beginning of wisdom?

Does Might Make Right?

Record your responses to the following questions in your Philosopher's Notebook.

- Describe an incident in which you got into an argument with someone with an aggressive discussion style (à la Thrasymachus). What was the outcome? Then describe how you might have adopted Socrates' "bull fighter" or "jujitsu" style in deflecting the aggression and moving the discussion in a more productive direction. How might the outcome have been different?

- There are many instances in everyday experience when people use a *might makes right* philosophy. For example:

  - "Why should you go to bed now? Because I'm your parent and I said so."

  - "I don't want to hear any more questions about my policy—that is, if you want to keep your job. The right thing for you to do is to follow the procedure I gave you."

  - "I gave you a low grade on your Shakespeare paper because your interpretation simply isn't right: it's too far out of what I consider to be the mainstream of scholarly critique."

Describe an incident in which someone has presented you with a *might makes right* philosophy of justice. Then compose a brief dialogue that explains how Socrates might have handled the situation.

Giving Birth to Ideas

Describe in your Philosopher's Notebook an educational experience you have had in which the teacher was able to help you "give birth" to your own knowledge or understanding. The experience could have been part of your schooling or in some other area of your life. What approach did the teacher use to stimulate you to develop your own independent ideas, rather than employing a more traditional, didactic approach? In what way was this approach analogous to that used by Socrates? How could such an approach be used in courses you are currently taking (or have taken)?

_____

_____

_____

_____

_____

_____

_____

_____

_____

_____

_____

_____

_____

_____

_____

_____

- When you think about your "self," what image comes to mind? Describe, as best you can, the entity that Socrates refers to as your "soul": that core identity that distinguishes you from every other living creature. Do you think this identity is immortal? Why or why not?

- Socrates posed the following challenge to his fellow citizens: ". . . are you not ashamed of heaping up the greatest amount of money and honour and reputation, and caring so little about wisdom and truth and the greatest improvement of the soul?" Do you think that this challenge is still relevant today? Explain your reasoning.

- Socrates believes that the most important truths already exist within our minds—we need only develop our powers of reflective analysis to discover them. Do you agree with this view? What might be examples of "truths" that exist within every person's mind?

- According to Socrates, no one knowingly does evil. Immoral conduct is always the result of ignorance, and if people are educated regarding the "right" way to act, they will necessarily do it. Do you agree with this view? Have you ever known the "right" thing to do, but suffered from a "failure of will" and ended up doing the wrong thing? If so, how would Socrates analyze your experience?

Influences on Character

Consider Socrates' central argument regarding education: would you agree that the formation of a person's thinking and character is typically the result of many influences throughout their lives? What influences have shaped your own personal development as an individual? Can you think of an example in which a single individual working in opposition to positive forces was able to corrupt someone? Some people believe that cult leaders are able to exert a brainwashing kind of influence on individuals. Contrast how their techniques for mind control are different from Socrates' method of questioning and dialectical exploration.

Emotional Appeals

Identify some examples of "false appeals to pity" that you have personally experienced: situations in which you or someone else has attempted to override the process of clear thinking by appealing for pity or sympathy. Was the appeal successful? Are there some circumstances in which such appeals are legitimate? Illegitimate?

_____

_____

_____

_____

_____

_____

_____

_____

_____

_____

_____

_____

_____

_____

_____

_____

THINK CRITICALLY

2.12

What Would I Die For?

Project yourself into Socrates' situation. Knowing that you will face the death penalty unless you can convince the court to be lenient, what would you say in your defense? What counter-penalty would you propose? Would your response be analogous to Socrates'? Why or why not?

Do I Know Myself?

Answer the following questions regarding your "self" as fully and specifically as you can.

- How would you describe your self?
- What are the qualities that differentiate you from all other selves?
- In what ways has your self changed during the course of your life? In what ways has it remained the same?
- How would you describe the relation of your self to your body?
- How are you able to come to know other selves? Do you think they are similar to or different from you?
- What do you think will happen to your self after you die? If you believe that your self will continue to exist in some form, will you be able to recognize other selves who have died? How?

_____

_____

_____

_____

_____

_____

_____

_____

_____

_____

_____

_____

_____

_____

_____

_____

_____

_____

Record your responses to the following questions in your Philosopher's Notebook.

- Compare Socrates' concept of the "soul" with your concept of the *self* which you described in the Think Philosophically activity on page 91. Did you view your "self" as a unified identity that remains the same over time?

  - an indissoluble entity that is immortal and will survive death?
  - an entity that is very different in kind from your physical body?
  - an entity that strives to achieve communion with some ultimate reality?

- In characterizing the relationship between the soul and the body, Socrates explains that the soul uses the body as "an instrument of perception," and that the soul "rules" the body in the same way that the divine rules the mortals. Do you agree with this analysis? Why or why not? How would you characterize the relationship between your soul/*self* and your body?

- Socrates argues that because the soul is of a unified, indissoluble form, we should not be concerned about death because the soul is incapable of being dispersed into nonexistence—it must be eternal. Does this argument address your fears about the potential death of your *self*/soul? Why or why not?

- For Socrates, our physical existence on earth is merely an imperfect reflection of ultimate and eternal reality, and our purpose in life is to achieve communion with this ultimate reality. How do his views compare with your perspective on the purpose of life? Do you believe that our goal in life is to achieve spiritual transcendence and/or intellectual enlightenment? If not, what do you believe is the purpose of your life?

THINK PHILOSOPHICALLY 3.3

Balancing Reason, Appetite, and Spirit

- Describe an experience in your life in which you experienced a vigorous conflict between the three dimensions of your *self* identified by Plato: Reason, Appetite, and Spirit. What was the nature of the conflict? How was it resolved?
- Describe an experience in your life in which Reason prevailed over Passion and Appetite. How was Reason able to prevail? Did you gain increased wisdom from the experience?
- Describe an experience in your life in which the three elements of your *self* identified by Plato worked together in a productive and harmonious fashion, enabling you to achieve a great success.

Seeking After Truth

- Explain your reaction to Descartes' challenge, "If you would be a real seeker after truth, it is necessary that at least once in your life you doubt, as far as possible, all things." Do you agree with this statement? Why or why not? If so, how?

- Describe some important areas of your life in which you would consider yourself to be a "real seeker after truth." Identify several examples of beliefs you had been taught or raised with which you questioned for the purpose of developing your own independent conclusions.

- Describe some important areas of your life in which, in your opinion, you *fell short* of being a "real seeker after truth." Identify several examples of beliefs you have been raised with that you have been reluctant to question. What factors have made it difficult for you to doubt these beliefs? Do you think you will critically analyze them at some point in the future?

My Body, My Self?

- Describe some of the ways your mind significantly affects your body: for example, when you are anxious, elated, depressed, in love (or lust), and so on.

- Describe some of the ways your body significantly affects your mind: for example, when you are feeling sick, deprived of sleep, taking medications, or finding yourself in a physically dangerous/threatening situation.

- Create your own metaphysical framework for the "*self*" by describing
  - your *self as thinking subject*.
  - your *self as physical body*.
  - your analysis of how these two aspects of your *self* relate to one another.

- Reconsider your views on human souls—what do you believe happens to the *self* after the death of the body? Why do you believe it? What would Descartes think of your views and your justification for them?

THINK PHILOSOPHICALLY   3.9
The Conscious Self

- Evaluate Locke's claim that your *conscious self* is not permanently attached to any particular body or substance. Do you agree with this view? Why or why not?

- Do you know anyone personally who has claimed to have lived a past life in another body? If so, do you think they would pass Locke's "test" for determining if their claim is authentic (having a clear memory of the *consciousness* of thinking and behaving as the previous individual)? Have you ever suspected that *your personal identity* lived a previous life? If so, how would Locke evaluate your belief?

- Locke believes that it is our memory that serves to link our *self* at this moment with our *self* in previous circumstances. But people's memories are often faulty. How can we distinguish between accurate memories of our *self* and inaccurate memories? To do so, don't we have to assume that we have a continuous *self* that is performing the evaluation? But since memory is supposed to explain the existence of our *self*, doesn't this mean that Locke's reasoning is circular? Explain your analysis of this dilemma.

Empiricism and the Self

- Perform your own empiricist investigation by examining the contents of your consciousness. What do you find there? Fleeting and temporary sensations, perceptions, and ideas, as Hume describes? Is your *self* anywhere to be found?

- Hume uses the terms *I* and *myself* throughout his writings, words that seem to suggest a continually existing *self-identity* that he is denying. Does Hume contradict himself? Why or why not?

- Descartes' key point was that even if we are dreaming, fantasizing or being deceived, the *act of doubting* proves that I have a *self* that is engaged in the activity of doubting. Is the same true for Hume? By denying the existence of a *self*, is he at the same time *proving* that his *self* exists, the *self* that is engaged in the act of denying? Why or why not?

- If you believe that you have a unifying and conscious *self* that exists through time, but you can't "catch yourself" when you examine your immediate experience, then where does your *self* exist? What is the nature of your *self* if you can't perceive it? (This is precisely the challenge taken up by our next philosopher, Immanuel Kant.)

- Imagine that you were present at the debate between King Menander and the monk Nagasena. How would you critically evaluate the arguments being made by both men? Do you think a chariot is an appropriate simile to the human self? Why or why not? How would you have responded to Nagasena's argument?

- Compare how Plato (in the *Phaedrus*) and Nagasena use the analogy of a chariot to explain the nature of the *self*. What are the similarities? What are the differences?

Searching for the Self

Here's an opportunity for you to be a philosophy detective engaged in a "missing person" investigation—looking for your *self*. If Kant is right, you should not be able to find your *self* among the contents of your consciousness. Instead, your *self* should be revealed as the synthesizing principle that unites your experience. Launch a reflective investigation into your *self*, and then describe as clearly as you can what you find. Did you discover your *self*? How would you describe the qualities of your *self*? In what ways is your *self* similar to all other selves? In what ways is your *self* different from all other selves?

_____

_____

_____

_____

_____

_____

_____

_____

_____

_____

_____

_____

_____

_____

Although the contents of the unconscious cannot be observed directly (according to Freud) we can observe them indirectly, like observing footprints in the sand or dusting for finger-prints. There are several areas in which unconscious influences are evident. This is an opportunity for you to look for evidence of unconscious functioning in each of these areas. Record your reflections in your Philosophy Notebook.

- *Slips of the tongue:* Think about a time in which you unexpectedly said what you *really* thought rather than what you intended to say: for example, "I think your new haircut looks *atrocious*" instead of your intended "I think your new haircut looks *attractive*." Do you think this is persuasive evidence for Freud's concept of the unconscious?

- *Dreams:* Describe a particularly disturbing dream, or a recurring dream, that expressed surprising or disturbing themes. What do you think the dream really meant? Do you think the dream is persuasive evidence for Freud's concept of the unconscious?

- *Neurosis:* Describe one sort of neurotic behavior in which you engage. (Don't worry, everyone has at least *one* neurosis!) For example, do you have a compulsion to check and recheck locks? To eat too much or too little? To perform superstitious rituals? To be overly suspicious ("paranoid") about others' intentions? To feel excessively guilty about something? To be chronically depressed? And so on. What do you think is the origin of this neurosis? Do you think this syndrome is persuasive evidence for Freud's concept of the unconscious?

3.15

Self as Behavior

- Think of someone you know and try to describe her solely in terms of her observable behavior. Then analyze your portrait: What aspects of her *self* does your description capture? What aspects of her *self* does your description omit?

- Now think about yourself. Assume the perspective of someone who knows you well and describe your *self* as he might see you, *based solely on your observable behavior*. What aspects of your *self* do you think his description would capture? What aspects of your *self* do you think his portrait of you would omit?

- Identify several of the defining qualities of your *self*: for example, empathetic, gregarious, reflective, fun-loving, curious, and so on. Then, using Ryle's approach, describe the qualities in terms of "a tendency to act a certain way in certain circumstances."

- Analyze your characterizations. Do your descriptions communicate fully the personal qualities of your *self* that you identified? If not, what's missing?

Accomplished writers often have a special talent for representing human experience in a rich, vibrant, and textured way. The French novelist **Marcel Proust** is renowned for articulating the phenomena of consciousness in a very phenomenological way. Consider the following descriptions of experiences and analyze their effectiveness from a phenomenological perspective on the *self*. Then compose your own description of an experience from a phenomenological point of view by detailing the phenomena of consciousness.

Think about some of the actions described at the beginning of this section. How would *you* explain why these people acted in the ways that they did? Which of these theories makes the most sense to you? Do you have your own theory to explain why people behave they way they do?

- A person commits an armed robbery, killing a guard in the process.
- A person embezzles large sums of money from the charitable organization that he directed.
- A firefighter risks her life to save the life of an infant trapped in a burning building.
- A peaceful protest gets out of control and turns into a violent and destructive altercation.
- A respected member of the community is accused of abusing the children on the teams that he coached.
- Two teenagers are accused of murdering their newborn infant and dumping the body in a garbage container.
- An 84-year-old woman who spent her life cleaning the homes of others donates her life savings—$186,000—to provide scholarships at a local college.

_____

_____

_____

_____

_____

_____

_____

_____

_____

_____

_____

_____

My Assumptions of Freedom

Think critically about your own assumptions regarding personal freedom by responding to the following questions:

- Do you believe that you can improve yourself by choosing freely to establish goals and make intelligent choices to achieve those goals? If so, do you believe that you are personally responsible for both the positive and "less positive" aspects of yourself? Why or why not?

- Do you believe that people are free to make independent choices in moral situations? Do you accept full responsibility for all of the moral choices you have made, even those you may regret having made? Why or why not?

- If you have religious beliefs, do you believe that you can influence your spiritual growth through the free choices that you make? Do you believe that people who make different religious choices than those prescribed by your religion are in spiritual jeopardy? Why or why not?

- Do you think that the problems of the world can be solved if people make more enlightened choices? Do you think that individuals in each society should be held responsible for the social problems of that society? Why or why not?

- Do you believe that people who commit crimes made free choices to do so? Why or why not? If so, how should they be held responsible for their actions? If not, what should happen to them?

- Do you believe that parents should raise children by encouraging them to think independently and accept responsibility for their choices? Why or why not?

- Consider a situation in which you felt you were at a crossroads, having to decide what path to take. d'Holbach argues that whatever choice you made, you *had* to make that choice because of the circumstances and motivations driving your action. Do you agree with this analysis? Why or why not? Do you believe that if you were able to be placed in an identical situation (with no recollection of the initial situation) that you would have the freedom to choose differently, or would your choice be the same? Why or why not?

- Imagine that you are engaged in a discussion with a determinist like d'Holbach over your freedom to choose. If that person says to you, "I know that you would never _____ because of the person you are," and you then go and _____, does that prove that you are capable of free choice? Why or why not?

- How do you think Mutius Scaevola would respond to d'Holbach's suggestion that in holding his hand in the fire, he was not making a free choice?

- How do you think Socrates would respond to d'Holbach's suggestion that in accepting his death sentence, he was not making a free choice?

- It seems as if d'Holbach's brand of determinism is not falsifiable: that because it can be invoked to explain *any* action, it can never ultimately be proved right or wrong. Is this a problem for determinism? Is this also a problem for analogous systems of belief like Freud's unconscious or the predictions of astrology? Why or why not?

Freedom, Choice, and Responsibility

- Reflect on Sartre's core belief that "existence precedes essence." Do you believe that your *self* (*soul*, *spirit* or *personality*) already existed before or at the moment of your birth? Or do you believe that you create your *essence* through the choices that you freely make? Explain the reasons for your response.

- Sartre's view of personal freedom is radical and uncompromising: we are "condemned" to be completely free and therefore we are completely responsible. Do you agree with this view? Why or why not?

- A number of factors seem to influence a person's development, including

  environmental experiences and learning
  genetic programming and inborn instincts
  social pressures and cultural socialization
  free choices

  Think about the blending of factors that has produced you as a person. How would you describe your unique "recipe"? Which factors have been most influential in your development? Have some factors had a particularly strong impact in certain areas of your life? How would Sartre respond to the idea that factors other than free choice contributed to your development (if you believe that they have)?

- Sartre believes that many people (perhaps all people to some extent) seek to "escape" from their freedom and responsibility. One indication of such escape attempts is denying the experience of existential emotions such as *anguish*, *abandonment*, and *despair*. Have you ever experienced these emotions in the profound, existential sense that Sartre believes is part of the human condition? Do you think experiencing these emotions is a useful barometer for determining your efforts to escape from your freedom?

- Later in life Sartre became a Marxist and modified his radical views on freedom, arguing that economic and political forces can limit freedom. Should this biographical fact influence our evaluation of these earlier views? Why or why not?

- Some people believe that Sartre's message, while disturbing, is ultimately inspiring and uplifting because of its emphasis on personal freedom and personal responsibility. What is your response to Sartre's basic ideas?

What Are the Limitations to My Freedom?

Making full use of your freedom involves first eliminating the constraints that limit your freedom. Use this thinking activity to begin this self-reflective process, which will prepare you for increasing your freedom.

- Identify some of the important *external constraints* or limitations on your options that are imposed by people or circumstances outside of you. Are there people in your life that actively seek to limit your freedom? Are you locked into situations that present limited opportunities? After identifying some of the significant external constraints, identify ways to diminish their impact on your freedom by either modifying or eliminating them.

- Evaluate the extent to which you are passively content to choose from a *limited selection of alternatives* that are presented to you. Identify several situations to begin actively creating your own possibilities.

- Identify some of the important *internal constraints* in your life using the following criteria to identify behaviors that:
  - you feel are out of your conscious control.
  - add negative results to your life.
  - you cannot provide a rational explanation for.

Increasing Your Freedom

Select areas of your life in which you would like to be more free: personal habits and behaviors, relationships with others, your career. Make a special effort to become aware of the constraints that are limiting your freedom and the internal messages that are shaping your thinking. Keep a record in your Philosopher's Notebook detailing your efforts and their result. Be sure to allow yourself sufficient time to escape from habitual forms and establish new patterns of thinking, feeling, and choosing. Cultivate the qualities of choosing freely that we explored in this section:

- Make freedom a priority.
- Accept your freedom and responsibility.
- Emphasize your ability to create yourself.
- Become aware of the constraints on your freedom.
- Create new options to choose from.

Think of someone you know whom you consider to be a person of outstanding moral character. This person doesn't have to be perfect—he or she doubtless has flaws. Nevertheless, this is a person you admire, whom you would like to emulate. After fixing this person in your mind, write down in your Philosopher's Notebook the qualities that this person displays that, in your mind, qualifies him or her as a morally upright individual. For each quality, try to think of an example of when the person displayed it. For example:

- **Moral courage:** *Charles is a person in my company who always takes the action he believes is morally "right," even though his point of view may be unpopular with many of the people present. Though he endured criticism, he never flinched or backed down, but instead defended his point of view with compelling reasons and stirring passion.*

If you have the opportunity, ask some people you know to describe their idea of a "moral person," and compare their responses to your own.

What Are My Moral Values?

You have many values—the guiding principles that you consider to be most important—that you have acquired over the course of your life. Your values deal with every aspect of your experience. The following questions are designed to elicit some of your values. Think carefully about each of the questions, and record your responses in your Philosopher's Notebook along with the reasons you have adopted that value. For example:

"I do believe that we have a moral obligation to those less fortunate than us. Why can a homeless person evoke feelings of compassion in one person and complete disgust in another? Over time, observation, experience, and intuition have formed the cornerstones of my beliefs, morally and intellectually. As a result, compassion and respect for others are moral values that have come to characterize my responses in my dealings with others. As a volunteer in an international relief program in Dehra Dun, India, I was assigned to various hospitals and clinics through different regions of the country. In Delhi, I and the other volunteers were overwhelmed by the immense poverty—thousands of people, poor and deformed, lined the streets—homeless, hungry, and desperate. We learned that over 300 million people in India live in poverty. Compassion, as Buddhists describe it, is the spontaneous reaction of an open heart. Compassion for all sentient beings, acknowledging the suffering and difficulties in the world around us, connects us not only with others but with ourselves."

Also, create your own ethical questions in the space provided. After you have completed this activity, examine your responses as a whole. Do they express a general, coherent, well-supported value system, or do they seem more like an unrelated collection of beliefs of varying degrees of clarity? This activity is a valuable investment of your time because you are creating a record of beliefs that you can return to and refine as you deepen your understanding of moral values.

- Do we have a moral responsibility towards less fortunate people?
- Is it wrong to divulge a secret someone has confided in you?
- Should we eat meat? Should we wear animal skins?
- Is it all right to tell a "white lie" to spare someone's feelings?
- Is it wrong to kill someone in self-defense?
- Should people be given equal opportunities, regardless of race, religion, or gender?
- Is it wrong to ridicule someone even if you believe it's in "good fun"?
- Should you "bend the rules" to advance your career?
- Is it all right to manipulate people into doing what you want if you believe it's for their own good?
- Is there anything wrong with pornography?
- Should we always try to take other people's needs into consideration when we act or should we first make sure that our own needs are taken care of?
- Should parents be held responsible for the misdeeds of their children?

Making Moral Decisions

The following are several dilemmas that ask you to respond with decisions based on moral reasoning. After thinking critically about each situation, do the following:

- Describe in your Philosopher's Notebook the decision that you would make in this situation and explain the reasons why. Identify the moral value(s) or principle(s) on which you based your decision.

- At the conclusion of the activity, compare the moral values that you used. Did you find that you used the same values to make decisions, or did you use different values?

- Based on this analysis, describe your general conclusions about your own "moral compass."

1. *The Lifeboat:* In 1842 a ship struck an iceberg and sank. There were 30 survivors, crowded into a lifeboat designed to hold just 7. With the weather stormy and getting worse, it was obvious that many of the passengers would have to be thrown overboard or the boat would sink and everyone would drown. Imagine that you were the captain of the boat. Would you have people thrown over the side? If so, on what basis would you decide who would go? Age? Health? Strength? Gender? Size? Survival skills? Friendships? Family?

2. *The Whistleblower:* Imagine that you are employed by a large corporation that manufactures baby formula. You suspect that a flaw in the manufacturing process results in contamination of the formula in a small number of cases, and that this contamination can result in serious illness and even death. You have been told by your supervisor that "Everything is under control," and you have been warned that if you "blow the whistle" by going public, you will be putting the entire company in jeopardy from multi-million-dollar lawsuits. You will naturally be fired and blackballed in the industry, and as the sole provider in your household, your family is depending on you. What do you do? Why?

3. *The Patient:* As a clinical psychologist, you are committed to protecting the privacy of your patients. One afternoon a patient tells you that her husband, a person who has been abusing her physically and mentally for years, has threatened to kill her, and she believes him. You try to convince her to leave him and seek professional help, but she tells you that she has decided to kill him. She is certain that he will find her wherever she goes and feels that she will only be safe when he is dead. What do you do?

4. *The Friend:* As the director of your department, you are in charge of filling an important vacancy. Many people have applied, including your best friend, who has been out of work for over a year and needs a job desperately. Although your friend would likely perform satisfactorily, there are several more experienced and talented candidates who would undoubtedly perform better. You have always prided yourself in hiring the best people, and you have earned a reputation as someone with high standards who will not compromise your striving for excellence. Whom do you hire?

THINK CRITICALLY

How "Ethically Subjective" Are My Ethics?

- Keeping in mind the issues discussed in this section, how would you respond to someone making the following statements:

  "In moral situations, you have to go with your inner feeling, what feels right."

  "What's right for one person may be wrong for someone else."

  "As long as you are being true to yourself, then you're morally right."

- In your own words, provide a clear definition of ethical subjectivism. What is attractive about this ethical theory? What are the fatal flaws that undermine the credibility of this approach?

- Identify some moral beliefs that an ethical subjectivist might hold but that you consider to be dangerous.

- Consider your own moral beliefs. What is the basis for your beliefs? Do any fall into the category of ethical subjectivism? Which ones? Why?

- Which moral beliefs do you consider to be based on the needs and interests of others rather than simply your personal feelings?

- Identify some moral beliefs that you consider to be self-evident, for instance:

  All people are created equal.

  Abusing children is wrong.

  Human slavery is unethical.

  Then explain why you consider your examples to be self-evident.

Cultural Relativism
and My Moral Perspective

- When we explored ethical subjectivism in the previous section, we saw that it seems to commit the naturalistic fallacy—trying to derive an "ought" from an "is." Can the same criticism be leveled against cultural relativism?

- Critics of cultural relativism have contended that it is self-contradictory. On the one hand, cultural relativists want to assert that there are absolutely *no* universal moral values that apply to all cultures. On the other hand, they seek to maintain that, as a universal value, members of one culture have no right to evaluate the moral values of another culture. Do you think this criticism of cultural relativism is valid? Why or why not?

- Cultural relativism seems to assume that in most cultures, the majority of people agree about basic moral values. Although this may be true in smaller, simpler cultures, this seems untrue with large, complex, modern cultures. How would a cultural relativist go about determining the prevailing view on moral values in a culture that is deeply divided? Is this a fatal flaw?

- The history of civilization includes individuals who stood alone against the prescribed moral values of their culture which they considered to be immoral. Who are some of these individuals? Why do so many people admire them? How would cultural relativism view these individuals: as courageous heroes and heroines or as abnormal deviants? Does this pose a problem for cultural relativism? Why?

- Several years ago a family that had immigrated to Minnesota was caught in a clash of cultural values. Consistent with cultural practices in his home country, the father of two daughters, aged 13 and 14, arranged marriages for them with two men in their thirties. The twin marriage ceremonies was an event of great celebration, with many friends and relatives attending. The day after the ceremony, the two young "brides" went to local law enforcement authorities, complaining about their situation. Their parents were arrested and charged with child endangerment and the two "grooms" were charged with statutory rape. All four adults stated that it never occurred to them that they were doing anything wrong. Nevertheless, they were convicted. How would Ruth Benedict analyze this event? How would you analyze this event?

Ethical Relativism
and My Moral Values

- Reflect on your own views regarding moral values. Do you live your life assuming that there are some universal moral values that apply to all cultures in all time periods? If so, identify which moral values these are. If not, explain how you would deal with someone whose moral values included hurting you.

- Imagine that you were engaged in a discussion with an ethical relativist. How would you use James's and Stace's criteria of "subjective satisfaction" and "rational explanation" to argue against their views.

- Consider the universal values that you identified in the first question (if you did, in fact, identify any). What is your foundation for these values, your justification for believing that these values apply not just to you but to other people as well, even though they may not agree with you? If you cited religious beliefs as part of your rationale, can you provide a justification for these values that is not based on religion?

- Imagine that you agree with the ethical relativists, believing that moral values are based entirely on group consensus. How would you go about identifying groups in your college or workplace? Which groups would qualify and which groups wouldn't? If the members of each group were not in complete accord, how would you recommend determining the group's values? What would you say to the "minority opinions" in each group?

- Do you agree with Stace that if people became convinced that ethical relativism was indeed true, that this would gradually have the effect of eroding their moral values to what we generally think of as less sophisticated, less enlightened levels? Why or why not?

THINK PHILOSOPHICALLY 5.8
Analyzing the Myth of Gyges

- Do you think that most people will break laws and violate traditional moral values if they're confident that they won't be caught? Identify one example that would support this thesis (for example, the looting that takes place during riots) and another example that contradicts it (returning a lost wallet that only you know you found).

- When you hear about someone who could have cheated or lied for their own benefit but refused to, do you consider them, in Glaucon's words, "a miserable fool"? Why or why not?

- If you found yourself in possession of the Ring of Gyges, identify three "immoral" things you might do by making yourself invisible that you ordinarily wouldn't do (for example, walking into a sold-out concert for which you couldn't buy tickets).

- Glaucon states that, "What people say is that to do wrong is, in itself, a desirable thing; on the other hand, it is not at all desirable to suffer wrong, and the harm to the sufferer outweighs the advantage to the doer." Socrates believes just the opposite, stating that "It is better to suffer wickedness than to commit it," and contending that doing wrong "will harm and corrupt that part of ourselves that is improved by just actions and destroyed by unjust actions." Identify which viewpoint you believe makes most sense, and explain your reasons for believing so.

THINK CRITICALLY

Religion and My Ethics

- If you were raised in a religious tradition, or you are currently involved in a religion, describe the ethical principles and values that are endorsed by your religion. Do you personally agree with all of these ethical beliefs? Why or why not?

- If participants in your religion were to be asked, "Why do you believe these ethical beliefs should be accepted by others?" what would be the response?

_____

_____

_____

_____

_____

_____

_____

_____

_____

_____

_____

_____

_____

_____

Natural Law and My Beliefs

- Identify three ethical principles that you personally believe reflect "natural laws" that are self-evident and that all people ought to ascribe to. If you don't personally believe that there are any such principles, then identify three such ethical principles that are incorporated into one or more religions (such as the Golden Rule).

- For each of the ethical principles that you just identified, describe a moral situation in which the principle would guide you in making an ethically appropriate decision.

- Aquinas ties his natural law ethic to a comprehensive religious theology. However, Aristotle argued that a belief in God is not necessary for the existence of natural law. Which point of view do you agree with? Why?

- "We hold these truths to be self-evident that all men are created equal, and that they are endowed by their Creator with certain inalienable rights, and that among these are life, liberty, and the pursuit of happiness." So begins the Declaration of Independence. Would this statement have the same authority if the phrase "endowed by their Creator" were replaced by the phrase "entitled by natural law"? Why or why not?

Hedonistic Calculus and Ethical Controversy

Imagine that you are a member of a student group at your college that has decided to stage the controversial play *The Normal Heart* by Larry Kramer. The play is based on the lives of real people and dramatizes their experiences in the early stages of the AIDS epidemic. It focuses on their efforts to publicize the horrific nature of this disease and to secure funding from a reluctant federal government to find a cure. The play is considered controversial because of its exclusive focus on the subject of AIDS, its explicit homosexual themes, and the large amount of profanity contained in the script. After lengthy discussion, however, your student group has decided that the educational and moral benefits of the play render it a valuable contribution to the life of the college.

While the play is in rehearsal, a local politician seizes upon it as an issue and mounts a political and public relations campaign against it. She distributes selected excerpts of the play to newspapers, religious groups, and civic organizations. She also introduces a bill in the state legislature to withdraw state funding for the college if the play is performed. The play creates a firestorm of controversy, replete with local and national news reports, editorials, and impassioned speeches for and against it. Everyone associated with the play is subjected to verbal harassment, threats, crank phone calls, and hate mail. The firestorm explodes when the house of one of the key spokespersons for the play is burned to the ground. The director and actors go into hiding for their safety, rehearsing in secret and moving from hotel to hotel.

Your student group has just convened to decide what course of action to take. Analyze the situation using the six criteria of the hedonistic calculus, and then conclude with your decision and the reasons that support your decision.

- Describe a moral decision involving other people that you made recently. Using Bentham's hedonistic calculus as a general guide, calculate what would have been the morally correct choice to make based on the principle of utility. How does this conclusion compare with the choice you actually made?

- Now analyze that same decision using Mill's distinction of "higher" and "lower" pleasures. What ethical conclusion does this method result in? Do you agree with Mill that "higher" pleasures have intrinsically greater value than "lower" pleasures? Why or why not? Use examples to support your conclusion.

- One major criticism of utilitarianism is its potential conflict with the principle of justice: that is, treating an individual unjustly so long as this leads to more overall happiness. For example, suppose the government is planning to execute a person they know to be innocent for the purpose of "setting an example." Create a scenario in which the utilitarians would have to support such an execution.

- In ancient Rome, innocent people—especially Christians—were slaughtered in the Coliseum for the entertainment and pleasure of thousands of people. How would the utilitarians analyze this situation?

- Explain why Mill believes that in calculating the greatest good for the greatest number of people that it is essential that you "be as strictly impartial as a disinterested and benevolent spectator."

- What do you think about only judging the consequences of actions to determine their moral worth, without reference to an individual's moral values, intentions, or motivations. Describe what role evaluating consequences plays in your moral reasoning? What other factors come into play in your efforts to "do the right thing"?

The Categorical Imperative and My Moral Compass

Using Kant's categorical imperative as a guide, analyze the following moral dilemmas to determine what the morally right course of action is. Be sure to explain your reasoning along with explaining your conclusion.

- Mired in a deep depression in which you believe that your life has no meaning and that there is no reason for going on, you contemplate suicide.

- Financial reverses have put you on the verge of bankruptcy and personal financial ruin. Your only hope is to borrow money, but you also know that there is virtually no chance that you will be able to repay the borrowed funds.

- You have been told that you possess a great talent in _____, and you are confident that you could fulfill your unique potential and accomplish great things in this area. But you are also lazy: the prospect of making the kind of commitment in time and energy to realize your talent seems daunting. Why not continue to enjoy the simple, relaxed pleasures of life rather than working so hard?

- Fortune has been good to you and you are financially very comfortable. You realize that many others are less fortunate than you, but your attitude is, "I wish them well, but they have to improve their lives on their own. I became a success by my own efforts—let them do the same."

THINK PHILOSOPHICALLY

What Is My Moral Character?

Reflect on the nature of your own moral character: how do you think others view you? Identify ten "moral character" terms that you think others might use to identify you (for example, compassionate, loyal, courageous, altruistic, just, patient, friendly, truthful, temperate). Then describe several moral situations in which you had an opportunity to display these qualities.

Do I Have a Virtuous Character?

- Identify and describe several moral decisions you have made recently. Then analyze the moral criteria that you used to make your decision: Did you focus on the *consequences* of the choice? Or on a moral *rule* that has objective authority? Or did you try to make a choice that reflects what a *virtuous person* would do? Or did you use a blending of all three ethical approaches, or another one of your own choosing?

- Do you agree with Aristotle that the ultimate goal all people strive for is happiness? Why or why not? Describe your concept of "happiness." How does it compare and contrast with that of Aristotle's notion of *eudaemonia*: "actively exercising your soul's powers in accord with virtue and reason"?

- Examine the Golden Mean virtues that Aristotle identifies as displayed in the chart on page 308. Do you agree with his formulations? What changes would you suggest? Create three more moral virtues in the same format:

  Vice (deficient)   Virtue (the mean)   Vice (excess)

- Identify and describe someone you believe to have a virtuous character. What virtuous qualities do they display on a consistent basis? How would you describe your own moral character? What moral virtues do you believe are prominent in your character? Which moral virtues would you like to strengthen?

_____

_____

_____

_____

_____

_____

_____

_____

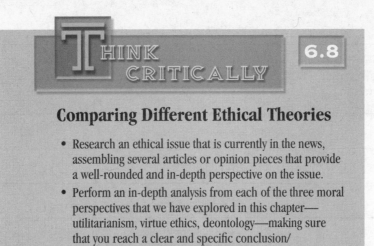

THINK CRITICALLY

Comparing Different Ethical Theories

- Research an ethical issue that is currently in the news, assembling several articles or opinion pieces that provide a well-rounded and in-depth perspective on the issue.

- Perform an in-depth analysis from each of the three moral perspectives that we have explored in this chapter—utilitarianism, virtue ethics, deontology—making sure that you reach a clear and specific conclusion/recommendation for each theory.

- Compare the various conclusions and forms of moral reasoning between the three theories. Which ethical perspective do you find to be most compelling? Why? Which ethical perspective do you find to be least compelling? Why?

- For Kierkegaard, the moral goal in life is to achieve *authenticity*, a state in which you fully and honestly accept your existential predicament: your freedom to choose your destiny, your independence of outside groups or individuals in defining your "self," your willingness to confront the uncertainties of the cosmos—including death and the meaning of life—with courage and resilience. With this as a criteria, evaluate to what extent you are living what Kierkegaard would consider an "authentic" life.

- Reflect on the forces that existentialists believe have alienated modern men and women, including the increasing dominance of technology; the complex size and structures of many businesses, bureaucracies, and social organizations; the manipulation by the media. In what ways have these forces affected you and the way you see yourself? For example, do you sometimes feel that you are being treated more as a Social Security number or a statistic than as a human being? Do you sometimes feel that it's difficult to forge meaningful relationships with other people in the professional or social groups of which you are a member? Have you felt disconnected from the jobs that you have had, being treated like a "cog" in a machine, or an impersonal paper-pusher?

- Consider society as a whole. To what extent do you believe that Kierkegaard's and Socrates' condemnations are on target?

  Let others complain that the age is wicked; my complaint is that it is wretched, for it lacks passion. Men's thoughts are thin and flimsy like lace, they are themselves pitiable like lacemakers. The thoughts of their hearts are too paltry to be sinful. For a worm it might be regarded as a sin to harbor such thoughts, but not for a being made in the image of God. Their lusts are dull and sluggish, their passions sleepy. They do their duty, these shopkeeping souls. . . . (Kierkegaard)

  You, my friend,—a citizen of the great and mighty and wise city of Athens,—are you not ashamed of heaping up the greatest amount of money and honour and reputation, and caring so little about wisdom and truth and the greatest improvement of the soul, which you never regard or heed at all? (Socrates)

- Evaluate Kierkegaard's analysis of how the abstraction of "the crowd" has usurped the concrete, living individual as the foundation of modern society. Do you agree with his analysis? Why or why not? Provide examples from your life and your experience with society to support your view.

- Do you agree with Kierkegaard that there has been a "leveling" of the individual: that you are seen by others primarily in terms of abstract categories rather than as a uniquely valuable individual? Why or why not?

- For Camus, Sisyphus is the *absurd hero* because of "his scorn of the gods, his hatred of death, and his passion for life." His existence is absurd because he pays for his passions by suffering "that unspeakable penalty in which the whole being is exerted toward accomplishing nothing." Why do you think Camus considers Sisyphus to be a "hero"? If Sisyphus is a model for human existence, how does Camus believe that we can also become heroes? Why do you think Camus believes that Sisyphus, at these moments of consciousness, "is superior to his fate . . . stronger than his rock"?

> It is during that return, that pause, that Sisyphus interests me. A face that toils so close to stones is already stone itself! . . . That hour like a breathing-space which returns as surely as his suffering, that is the hour of consciousness. At each of those moments when he leaves the heights and gradually sinks toward the lairs of the gods, he is superior to his fate. He is stronger than his rock.

- For Camus, "Crushing truths perish from being acknowledged," liberating us to discover meaning and happiness. "Ancient wisdom confirms modern heroism" in the remarkable words of Oedipus, "Despite so many ordeals, my advanced age and the nobility of my soul make me conclude that all is well." What does Camus believe we have to do, as modern men and women living in an absurd world, in order for us to also conclude that "all is well"?

- Camus believes that despite his eternal torment, Sisyphus is joyful because "His fate belongs to him." "The universe henceforth without a master seems to him neither sterile nor futile. Each atom of that stone, each mineral flake of that night filled mountain, in itself forms a world. The struggle itself toward the heights is enough to fill a man's heart. One must imagine Sisyphus happy."

Reflect on your own life: even if you were to conclude that there is no benevolent God nor ultimate purpose to life, do you think that your life could still be meaningful and happy? Why or why not?

- The ethics of care is based on *empathy*, a complex intellectual and emotional identification with another person. Think of a recent situation in which you felt empathy toward someone else, and describe what the experience felt like as specifically as you can.

- Reflect on several of the moral decisions that you have made recently. What role has the ethics of care played in your moral reasoning?

- In your own words, explain what you think Noddings means by the concept of "grasping the reality of the other as a possibility for myself."

- Do you agree with Noddings' distinction between "natural caring" and "ethical caring"? Why or why not? What is your reaction to Noddings' statement that "I am not obliged to care for starving children in Africa, because there is no way for this caring to be completed in the other unless I abandon the caring to which I am obligated"?

THINK PHILOSOPHICALLY

My Religious Beliefs

As you respond to the following questions, express your ideas thoughtfully and articulately. If you have no religious beliefs at this time, respond to these questions with reference to a religion with which you are familiar.

- What is your definition of religion? What do you think is the purpose of religion?
- How would you describe your religious beliefs? Does it include a belief in "God"? If so, describe your concept of God.
- What was the origin of your religious beliefs (or lack of religious beliefs)? If your beliefs are different from those you were raised with, explain what caused you to change your religious views.
- What religious activities do you engage in (for example, worship, prayer, meditation, communion, singing, chanting, liturgy)?
- Describe the role that religious leaders and "holy books" play in your religion.
- Describe some of the "symbols" and "myths" of your religion.
- How does your religion view religions that are different?

My Concept of Religion

Describe your concept of religion as specifically as possible. Where did the concept originate for you? How has it evolved as you have matured? Explain the reasons or experiences that support your concept.

Evaluate your concept of religion by answering the following questions, which are designed to help you develop a sufficiently broad and precise concept of religion:

- Does your definition reduce religion to what you happen to be acquainted with by accident of birth and socialization?

- Does your definition reflect a bias on your part—positive or negative—toward religion as a whole, or toward a particular religion?

- Does your definition limit religion to what it has been in the past, and nothing else, or does your definition make it possible to speak of emerging forms of religion?

Compare your definition of religion to the definitions of other students in your class. What are the similarities? What are the differences? How do you explain these similarities and differences?

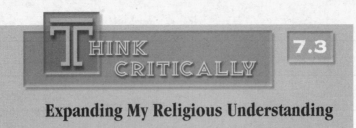

THINK CRITICALLY

Expanding My Religious Understanding

- Reflect on the religions that we reviewed in this chapter (indigenous, Buddhism, Hinduism, Taoism, Judaism, Christianity, Islam) as well as other religions with which you are familiar. Identify several common themes that you find to be particularly significant.

- Explain as best you can the reasons these themes resonate with you, and describe how these themes might relate to your life. Provide specific examples.

- Nietzsche grounds his religious and moral philosophy on what he considers to be a basic principle found at the core of life—"an incarnate will to power, it will strive to grow, spread, seize, become predominant—not from any morality or immorality but because it is *living* and because life simply *is* will to power." Do you agree with this characterization of a basic life force? Why or why not?

- What does Nietzsche mean by his arresting pronouncement that "God is dead"? What are his reasons for coming to this conclusion?

- Exploitation and domination are natural consequences of the *will to power*, according to Nietzsche. Rather than see them as "immoral" we should recognize them as essential attributes of the strong and noble individual. Critically evaluate this view and provide an example of your perspective.

- Because the majority of individuals are weak, insecure, and lacking in determination, Nietzsche believes that they conspire to create a system of values to drag down superior individuals and keep them in check. Have you ever personally experienced a situation in which you distinguished yourself in some way, only to find yourself the target of envy and criticism from others? If so, does this experience support Nietzsche's thesis regarding the "slave morality"?

- What are the implications of Nietzsche's views? In other words, suppose the majority of individuals took his exhortations to heart and became superior "overmen," seeking to dominate and exploit those around them. What would be the result?

- Have you ever had a "mystical experience," religious or otherwise? If so, did it meet the four "marks" that James identifies?

- In attempting to assess the "warrant for truth" of mystical states, James concludes that, "Mystical states, when well developed, usually are, and have the right to be, absolutely authoritative over the individuals to whom they come." In other words, as outsiders, we should presume the authenticity of mystical claims of others, and not try to denigrate or undermine their legitimacy. Do you agree with this point? Why or why not?

- Although James believes that we should acknowledge the potential authenticity of mystical states, we are under no obligation to "accept their revelations uncritically." In other words, we still have a responsibility to think philosophically about the mystical claims of others, even while recognizing the reality of these experiences for those having them. Does this point make sense to you? Why or why not?

- James's final point is his most important, from an epistemological standpoint. By accepting the potential authenticity of mystical experiences, we are acknowledging that there are epistemologically legitimate states of consciousness other than the "rationalistic, non-mystical" state, and that this recognition opens out "the possibility of other orders of truth, in which, so far as anything in us vitally responds to them we may freely continue to have faith." And by including mystical states in our worldview, James believes that we create a vision of a wider, more inclusive world. What is your evaluation of James's view? What other authentic "states of consciousness" might you include in the world in addition to "rationalistic states" and "mystical states"?

Evaluating Arguments for Religion

- Reflect on the three cosmological argument's for existence that we explored in this section:
  - The argument from contingency
  - The argument from design
  - The argument from morality

Evaluate each of the arguments in terms of how persuasive you find it. What are its strongest points? What are its weakest points?

- Evaluate Bertrand Russell's critique of the first cause argument and the argument from design. Do you agree with his analysis? Why or why not?

- How would you respond to the question, "Do you believe in God?" If you would respond "Yes," describe what arguments you would use to explain the rationale for your belief. If you would respond "No," describe the reasoning you would use to explain your conclusion.

- Create an argument for the existence (or nonexistence) of God that is different from those we examined in this section. Try the argument out on someone you know and describe their reactions. Did they find the argument persuasive? Why or why not?

- Russell believes that, overall, religion has been a negative force in human experience. Imagine that you were engaged in a discussion with him: compose a Socratic dialogue that examines his criticisms of organized religion.

- Do you think that the problem of evil poses a threat to the possibility of a God who is omnipotent and all-loving? Explain your reasoning.

- Hick maintains that if God interfered with the creation or development of people that we would be like "helpless puppets" or patients "acting out a series of posthypnotic suggestions" because it would undermine free choice. Do you agree with this reasoning? For example, aren't individuals already born with inherited traits that influence their personality development and subsequent choices? Couldn't God simply prevent the creation of truly evil individuals without affecting the freedom of the vast majority of people?

- Hick also maintains that if God prevented natural disasters from occurring it would mean negating all of the laws of science. Do you agree with this reasoning? For example, couldn't God have created a scientifically orderly world in which natural disasters did not cause such human catastrophes?

- According to Hick, the sorrows, tragedies, and disappointments of this world are necessary ingredients in "soul-making." Do you agree with this way of thinking? How have the tragedies in your life influenced you? Might some disasters be positive influences, whereas others are simply destructive?

- Because there is not enough time on this earth for our souls to become sufficiently enlightened, Hick believes that this suggests there must be an afterlife in which this process is continued. Does this reasoning make sense to you? Why or why not?

- Does the problem of evil in the world influence your thinking about religion? Why or why not? If you have a belief in God, how do you reconcile the existence of evil with your concept of God?

- After reading this article, look closely at a piece of furniture that is within your field of vision: Is the piece of furniture *real*? How do you *know* if it's real or not? Explain your reasoning for both responses.

- Russell analyzes the table near him in terms of its color, texture, and shape, and concludes:

  > Thus it becomes evident that the real table, if there is one, is not the same as what we immediately experience by sight or touch or hearing. The real table, if there is one, is not *immediately* known to us at all, but must be an inference from what is immediately known.

  Do you agree with Russell's conclusion? Why or why not?

- Russell goes on to observe: "Hence, two very difficult questions at once arise; namely, (1) Is there a real table at all? (2) If so, what sort of object can it be?" Explain how you would respond to these two questions, and explain the reasoning for your conclusions.

- Russell's article emphasizes the significance of the philosophical distinction between *appearances* (what things seem to be) and *reality*, (what they are). After "thinking philosophically" about these issues, do you see the world around you in a new light? Explain your response and the reasons for it.

Is Knowledge Innate?

- Do you find Socrates' example of the slave boy's "recollection" of geometric principles that he has not been explicitly taught to be persuasive? Why or why not? Can you think of an alternative explanation for the slave boy's "knowledge"? What else might be going on besides recollection when we see the correctness of the claim that to double the area of square we should use the length of the original diagonal for the new sides.

- Reflect on your own intellectual development. Can you identify knowledge of which you became aware that you did not learn from experience? For example, your belief in the scientific law of cause and effect. Although you may experience events connected to other events, there is nothing in experience that "teaches" you that this connection is a necessary one. Other examples might include your knowledge of logic, mathematics, language, moral principles, or religious insight.

- Imagine that you disagreed with Socrates' concept of innate knowledge learned in a previous perfect world before birth. Explain how you would go about trying to convince Socrates that he was wrong.

- If you believe that there is innate knowledge independent of experience, and you reject Socrates' idea of a perfect world where immortal souls exist before birth, then how would you explain the origin of these innate ideas—in other words, where did they come from?

- Explain how the images projected on the back wall of Plato's cave are similar to the images we perceive on the television, or the images that are communicated through newspapers, magazines, and books. Why do the people in Plato's cage believe that the perceptual images they are viewing projected on the wall are "real"? Why do people who view television and read information sources uncritically tend to believe that what they are viewing is "real"?

- Explain why recognizing that the perceptions we encounter in our daily lives are often incomplete, inaccurate, and distorted is essential to beginning our journey from the dark depths of ignorance toward the illumination of understanding.

- In Plato's allegory, discarding ignorant beliefs and embracing the truth can be a disturbing process, as we are forced to see things objectively, illuminated as they really are, rather than shrouded in the shadows of bias and distortion. Describe an experience in which achieving a knowledgeable, truthful insight was a disturbing experience for you.

    - Education then is the art of doing this very thing, this turning around, the knowledge of how the soul can most easily and most effectively be turned around; it is not the art of putting the capacity of sight into the soul; the soul possesses that already but it is not turned the right way or looking where it should. This is what education has to deal with.

Plato believes that the view of knowledge embodied in the Allegory of the Cave has profound and far-reaching implications for education. Explain what you believe Plato means by saying that genuine education involves, "turning one's whole soul from the world of becoming until it can endure to contemplate reality" *instead of* "putting the capacity of sight into the soul." Describe two examples from your own educational experience, one which involved "turning your whole soul towards reality" and another in which you attempted to "put the capacity of sight into your soul."

- Evaluating your life as a whole, at what stage in Plato's allegory would you place yourself? Why?

THINK CRITICALLY

How Informed Are My Philosophical Beliefs?

One of the core elements of thinking philosophically is reflecting thoughtfully on your intellectual development. Make a list of the philosophical themes that you have studied in your Introduction to Philosophy course (your professor may choose to have the class do this as a group). Then, for each of these topics, write a paragraph assessing the relative strength (or weakness) of your beliefs in that area. For example:

> After studying the issues related to developing enlightened values, and exploring a variety of different ethical theories, I believe that I am on my way to developing a thoughtful approach to moral decisions of which I feel confident. Some of my central moral principles include. . . . A recent example of a challenging moral decision in which I applied ethical approach was. . . .

Be sure that your responses are both honest and specific. They represent a rough evaluation of the progress you have made in learning to think philosophically about the most difficult areas of life. This is a journey that you will continue for the rest of your life, and ongoing critical reflection is the tool you can use to chart your growth and ensure that you are on the path you wish to take.

Evaluating the Accuracy of My Beliefs

State whether you think that each of the following beliefs is

- *completely accurate* (so that you would say, "I know this is the case").
- *generally accurate* but not completely accurate (so that you would say, "This is often, but not always, the case").
- *generally not accurate* but sometimes accurate (so that you would say, "This is usually not the case but is sometimes true").
- *definitely not accurate* (so that you would say, "I know that this is not the case").

After determining the degree of accuracy in this way, explain why you have selected your answer.

Beliefs to be evaluated

- I believe with Socrates that "the unexamined life is not worth living."
- I believe that the *self* is that unifying force that synthesizes our experiences into a personal identity.
- I believe in the existence of a supernatural Creator that I call "God."
- I believe that your astrological sign determines your basic personality traits.
- I believe that people are completely free and so completely responsible for their choices.
- Your example of a belief:

Example: I believe that if you treat other people with respect and consideration, that they will reciprocate and treat you the same way.

> *Degree of accuracy:* Generally, but not completely, accurate.
>
> *Explanation:* Although treating other people with respect and consideration may inspire many people to reciprocate with the same treatment, this is not likely to be true in all cases.

- Have you ever had the experience of wondering whether much of what you had been brought up to believe as true was in fact unreliable? If so, identify some of the main beliefs or values that you called into question. Was there a particular event that stimulated this process of doubt and examination? What was the outcome of your reflective questioning?

- Try to replicate Descartes' reflective process. Describe your current situation as you are reading this text, just as he does. Then try to trace his pattern of thinking: Can you imagine that what you think is real is actually a dream? How can you be sure? Haven't you had dreams that were at least as realistic as the current situation in which you now find yourself? Is there any clear criteria you can use to differentiate between when you are dreaming and when you are awake?

- Descartes' "evil genius" bears an uncanny resemblance to the evil forces in the film *The Matrix*. In that film the central character, Neo, is faced with a provocative choice: Does he want to continue existing in a "virtual" world, which is pleasant but unreal, a manipulated reality created by evil forces? Or does he wish to experience the real world, which is unpleasant and dangerous? If you were presented with these alternatives, which would you choose? Why? Is there any resemblance between this type of choice and the one suggested by John Stuart Mill, between being a "contented fool" or a "discontented Socrates"? Why or why not?

- Try to replicate Descartes' foundational starting point, "I think, therefore I am." Does your ability to think convince you, for once and for all, that you exist? What does it mean to you to say, "I exist"? Exactly how would you describe the "I" that exists?

- Take Locke's challenge again, this time writing out your responses. Carefully examine your own thoughts: can you identify any ideas that did not come from the experiences of sensations or reflections on these experiences?

- Locke believes that it is contradictory to believe that we might possess knowledge of which we are unaware. Do you agree with his position? Why or why not?

- Even though Locke believes that we can only have direct knowledge of the mental images and impressions in our mind, he does not believe this should cause us to doubt the existence of an external world that produces these images and impressions. Do you agree with his analysis? Why or why not?

- Locke provides a number of arguments for the existence of the external world of which we can have no direct knowledge:

   Common sense tells us that the world exists.

   God would not deceive us regarding the existence of the external world.

   People who raise philosophical doubts about the existence of the external world (like Descartes) should place their hand in a fiery furnace to be convinced.

   If we were to doubt such basic convictions as the external world, we would become paralyzed by inaction and perish.

   Do you find any of these arguments for an external world persuasive? Which ones? Why? Can you think of any additional arguments that Locke might use?

- Describe an instance in which you were convinced that you had perceived something that turned out to be very different from what you came to believe actually occurred. How does this sort of experience pose a problem for Locke?

- Describe, in your own words, your own epistemology. How do you think we gain knowledge?

- What is your reaction to Berkeley's claim that the only things that exist in the universe are minds and ideas that exist in the minds? If you are not comfortable with his eliminating an independently existing external world, how would you go about refuting his ideas?

- Unfortunately, Berkeley's major writings were published after Locke's death. If he had still been alive, how do you think Locke would have responded to Berkeley's criticism of his views?

- Samuel Johnson, a famous English writer who lived at the same time as Berkeley, responded to Berkeley's subjectivist idealism by kicking a stone and sending it flying into the air, while saying, "I refute him thus." Do you think this is a persuasive "argument" by Johnson? Why or why not?

- Berkeley's response to the criticism of common sense by Johnson and others was

> But after all, say you, it sounds very harsh to say we eat and drink ideas, and are clothed with ideas. I acknowledge it does so—the word idea not being used in common discourse to signify the several combinations of sensible qualities which are called things; and it is certain that any expression which varies from the familiar use of language will seem harsh and ridiculous. But this doth not concern the truth of the proposition, which in other words is no more than to say, we are fed and clothed with those things which we perceive immediately by our senses. The hardness or softness, the colour, taste, warmth, figure, or suchlike qualities, which combined together constitute the several sorts of victuals and apparel, have been shewn to exist only in the mind that perceives them; and this is all that is meant by calling them ideas; which word if it was as ordinarily used as thing, would sound no harsher nor more ridiculous than it. I am not for disputing about the propriety, but the truth of the expression. If therefore you agree with me that we eat and drink and are clad with the immediate objects of sense, which cannot exist unperceived or without the mind, I shall readily grant it is more proper or conformable to custom that they should be called things rather than ideas.

Imagine that you are Berkeley, and describe the series of perceptions that would constitute Samuel Johnson's kicking the stone.

_____

_____

_____

_____

_____

_____

_____

_____

THINK PHILOSOPHICALLY

Analyzing David Hume

- Do you agree with Hume that appealing to the existence of God in order to support the belief that there is an external world (as Locke and Berkeley do) amounts to philosophical hypocrisy? Why or why not?

- Summarize Hume's arguments that it is impossible for us to ever have certain knowledge of the principle of cause and effect, whether we are rationalists or empiricists. Do you agree with his reasoning? Why or why not? Construct an argument to convince Hume that the principle of cause and effect is indeed valid, being sure to provide examples to support your point of view.

- Imagine that you truly believed that the principles of cause and effect and induction were in fact not "knowledge" at all but merely habitual associations. Would this conclusion influence any aspect of your life? Explain why or why not.

- Hume makes a sharp distinction between the skepticism of his philosophical reasoning and the contented optimism of the way he lives his life. What do you think of this "split" between rational/theoretical arguments and lived experience? Do you think that our choices in life should necessarily reflect our epistemological convictions? Describe an example to support your point of view.

- Hume believes that all metaphysical beliefs (that is, any belief not based on direct sense experience) should be "committed to the flames" because it cannot be empirically justified. This would include all beliefs regarding God, human freedom, universal moral laws, and so on. Do you agree with Hume? If not, explain how you would go about rebutting his arguments.

How Do I Construct Knowledge?

For Kant, we constitute our world through the ongoing synthesis of the categories of our mind with the sensations of experience. We have seen in this section that this perceiving is a dynamic process in which we actively select, organize, and interpret sensations in a way that reflects our unique perceiving "lenses." To construct knowledge from the information provided from experience, we must explore many different perspectives on the focus of our attention and take into account the "lenses" of the individuals or organizations that are providing the information—as well as being acutely aware of our own "lenses." This type of organized evaluation of contrasting sources and opinions—"perspective taking"—is an essential strategy of sophisticated thinking and one of the most powerful ways to construct well-supported beliefs and genuine knowledge. To experience this epistemological process in action, let's examine three different media accounts of the assassination of Malcolm X as he was speaking at a meeting in Harlem. As you read through the various accounts, pay particular attention to the different perceptions each one presents of this event. You will note that each account viewed the event through its own perceiving lenses, which shaped and influenced the information the writer selected, the way the writer organized it, his or her interpretations of the event and the people involved, and the language used to describe it. After you have finished reading the accounts, analyze some of the differences in these perceptions by answering the following questions. As you do this, try to begin constructing your own "knowledge" of this event.

- What details of the events has each writer *selected* to focus on?
- How has each writer *organized* the details selected? Remember that most newspapers present what they consider the most important information first and the least important last.
- How does each writer *interpret* Malcolm X, his followers, the gunmen, and the significance of the assassination?
- How has each author used language to express his or her perspective and to influence the reader's thinking?
- After critically evaluating these various sources, compose your own account of this event, as if you were writing for a major news organization. You may integrate additional research that you do into the event.

- Why does Kant say that Hume's ideas "first interrupted my dogmatic slumber, and gave my investigations in the field of speculative philosophy quite a new direction"?
- Explain why Kant suggests that his approach embodies a "Copernican revolution" in epistemology. What are the central differences between his epistemology and that of the rationalists and the empiricists?
- Why is the concept of "perceiving lenses" a useful metaphor in illustrating the way in which we actively constitute our world?
- What is the meaning of Kant's famous quote, "Thoughts (concepts) without content (sense data) are empty; intuitions (of sensations) without conceptions, blind"?
- Explain the significance of Kant's observation that "There can be no doubt that all our knowledge begins with experience. . . . But though all our knowledge begins with experience, it does not follow that it all arises out of experience."
- The empiricists concluded that we can never "know" that the principle of cause and effect is valid or that the external world exists independently of our perception of it. How does Kant's approach seek to overcome these troubling conclusions?
- What are the phenomenal and noumenal realities, and why does Kant believe in their existence?
- Kant believes that the following transcendental ideas are necessary to explain our experience of the universe: Self, Cosmos, God. Considering each of these "regulative" ideas in turn, analyze whether or not you agree that the idea is required to explain the way we experience the world.

- Reflect on your study of philosophy to this point. Identify five emotions that you believe play a significant role in thinking philosophically, and explain your rationale. Be sure to include specific examples to illustrate your points.

- Jaggar believes that both philosophy and modern science have artificially separated reason and emotion, and have designated reason as the one true way of achieving knowledge and truth. Do you agree with her reasoning? Why or why not?

- Jaggar identifies the following components of what we mean by the term/concept *emotion*

    A physiological sensation or feeling

    Intentional judgment

    Social construct

    Active engagement/conscious choice

    Select a complex emotion and analyze its structure by explaining how each of these factors contributes to its meaning.

- Jaggar believes that modern science needs to elevate emotions to play a prominent role in every aspect of scientific exploration, though she doesn't provide many concrete examples to examine. Identify one emotion that you believe should be an essential and consistent element in scientific inquiry, and explain (briefly) how this emotion might be better integrated into the process of constructing knowledge.

Reflect on the social and political structure of your society by responding to the following questions:

- *Issues of Justice:* In what ways does your society distribute resources to its citizens? In what ways does it make opportunities for education and to acquire available resources? To what extent are people treated equally? In what ways would you consider your society to be "just"?

- *Issues of Law:* How does your society justify its existence and its laws? To what extent are its "civic laws" based on "natural laws" that are thought to apply to all humans in all societies? To what extent are the laws applied fairly to people, regardless of their wealth, social status, gender, or racial identity? How does your society treat people who disagree with and disobey its laws? How are people who engage in "civil disobedience" treated (for example, those who act disruptively to protest social policies or war policies with which they disagree)?

- *Issues of Public Interest:* In what ways does your society support the well-being of its less advantaged citizens (for example, those who are poor, elderly, unemployed, sick, abused, or neglected)? In what ways are citizens expected to sacrifice their individual interests to support the general interest (for example, paying taxes)? In what ways does your society help those who are unable to help themselves? How does it promote the general good through regulations and economic support?

- *Issues of Duty:* What specific obligations and duties are citizens in your society responsible for performing (for example, serving on juries)?

- *Issues of Rights:* What individual rights do citizens in your society expect to have (for example, the right to practice the religion of their choice)? What rights does your society consider to be "universal" in the sense that they are rights that all people in all societies should enjoy?

- *Issues of Freedom:* What are the basic freedoms that your society guarantees for all of its citizens (for example, freedom to express your views without being arrested or harassed)? In what areas are personal freedoms limited in your society?

- *Issues of Power and Influence:* How is power acquired and administered in your society? What can citizens do to influence social policies and laws?

- Plato's concern about democratic forms of government was that many citizens are ill-informed about important issues and vulnerable to being manipulated by those in power. When you examine the current state of affairs in our society, do you believe that there is evidence to support Plato's concern regarding the dangers of democracy? If so, what alternatives would you propose to address these concerns, other than altering the democratic form of government?

- One of the major critiques of Plato's ideas about social justice is that the Athenian system was dependent on a large slave population for its functioning, individuals who are left out of Plato's conception of an ideal state. How do you think Plato would respond to the criticism that his ideas lack validity because of his acceptance of slavery? (The same question can be posed to the founding fathers of America who, like Thomas Jefferson, supported the institution of slavery while advocating "inalienable rights" of life, liberty, and the pursuit of happiness for everyone else.)

- Critically evaluate Plato's basic assumption that people fall into one of three classes: guardians, warriors, or workers. For example, do such natural classes exist? How would one go about determining which group people should be placed in? At what point in a person's life do their abilities become clearly delineated? Is it possible for people to develop abilities later in life that may not have been obvious earlier on? Is their a danger of prematurely classifying people and creating a "self-fulfilling prophecy" for their destinies? Who would make the decision?

- Many people assume "egalitarianism" as a core value today, the idea that every person is created intrinsically equal and that they are entitled to certain basic rights and freedoms. How would you go about defending this point of view to Plato?

- Aristotle believes that humans are first and foremost social creatures who can only fulfill their potential as members of a social community, and that people who could exist independently of human community must be either a "beast or a god." Do you agree? Why or why not?

- According to Aristotle the state is "prior to the individual," suggesting that the public interest of the community takes precedence over the interests of a few individuals. For example, imagine the state wants to construct a new road to alleviate traffic congestion, and that the proposed route runs right through a neighborhood where you and other families have lived for decades. What do you think Aristotle's reaction would be if it was his house that was being demolished? What would your reaction be? Is there a difference in the two reactions? If so, why?

- Aristotle believed that "slaves" were fulfilling their natural function in society by promoting the general interest for all. He also argued that if slaves were freed, they would be unhappy and unable to cope with the challenges of living. Assume that you disagree with Aristotle: what arguments would you make to convince him that his view of slaves is unjust? How might he respond?

- Aristotle also believed that women should not be considered the equals of men, and that fulfilling their potential meant recognizing and accepting their secondary status. Assume that you disagree with Aristotle: what arguments would you make to convince Aristotle that his view is mistaken? How might he respond?

- Justice, for Aristotle, is the result of each person fulfilling his or her natural potential, which would result in a hierarchical but cooperative society. Critically evaluate this definition of "justice."

- In sharp contrast to Aristotle's view that humans are naturally social and political animals, Hobbes believes that being alone is our natural state, and that we form social relationships only out of necessity and personal self-interest. Identify which viewpoint you find more compelling and explain your reasoning.

- Hobbes believes that people are naturally competitive with one another, and that in the absence of laws to keep these impulses in check, we would do whatever it takes to gain wealth, power, and glory. Try to imagine a society in which there were no laws or police or justice system to protect people from one another. Describe what you think would happen to society and our social relationships over the period of a year.

- Have you ever been in a situation in which the normal social rules broke down? For example, in the middle of an out-of-control mob, a panic situation involving other people, or a competitive activity in which people's emotions got out of hand? Describe what it felt like to be in this situation, and analyze its dynamics from Hobbes's point of view.

- Hobbes believes that his rather pessimistic views are supported by our experiences: we take extraordinary precautions to protect ourselves and our possessions, and that when we look at world events, we see ongoing examples of war, oppression, cruelty, competition, hatred, and genocide. Do you think that this is a persuasive argument for Hobbes's view of human nature? Why or why not?

- According to Hobbes, the ideas of "justice" and "injustice" only come into existence when laws are created: they have no natural existence or authority. Do you agree with this perspective? Why or why not?

- Locke believes that even when people do not live in organized societies with laws and justice systems, they are nevertheless bound by the "law of nature," reflecting God's will. Do you agree with this view? Why or why not? If so, what values and stipulations are a part of the law of nature?

- As the "servant" of the people, Locke believed that the political state should be rebelled against and dissolved if it fails to perform its functions under the social contract. What policies would your government have to adopt for you to support the idea of rebelling against it?

- In some passages Locke's "state of nature" seems to be a utopian paradise; in others, a perilous existence fraught with dangers from others. If a group of people were placed in a situation in which they were living outside the laws of the state (for example, analogous to the novel *Lord of the Flies* or the television show "Survivor" but without rules and cameras), which version of Locke's "state of nature" would be most likely to occur? Why?

- Locke believes that all people retain the right to control their own bodies and are entitled to a fair share of whatever they produce through their own labor. Do you agree with this view? Why or why not? Can you think of any exceptions to this perspective (for example, someone contemplating suicide)?

- Thomas Jefferson changed Locke's statement of inalienable rights from "Life, liberty and property" to "Life, liberty and the pursuit of happiness." How does the meaning of these two formulations differ? Which one do you think is more appropriate for the Declaration of Independence? Why?

Creating a Just Society

We began this chapter with the challenge: "Imagine that you were given the project of creating a society based on the principle of justice: how would you go about it and how would you justify your proposed state?" Using Rawls's concept of the "veil of ignorance," identify what principles of justice you would base your society on in the areas of

- Rights and liberties
- Economic opportunity
- Education
- Allocation of wealth and property
- Health care
- Political representation
- Other areas you believe are important

- In analyzing the concept of justice, Mill distinguishes between the conceptual meaning of the term and the emotions associated with the idea of justice. What is the conceptual meaning of *your* concept of justice? What emotions do you associate with your idea of justice? Are these two dimensions of your notion of justice consistent?

- Identify the five different definitions of justice that Mill describes. Which of these definitions are also a part of your definition of justice? Mill believes that these definitions ultimately depend on the principle of social utility. Do you agree?

- Do you agree with Mill's statement that "Over himself, over his own body and mind, the individual is sovereign"? Why or why not? Identify several examples that would provide clear exceptions to this principle.

- Critically evaluate the following statement:

    The only freedom which deserves the name, is that of pursuing our own good in our own way, so long as we do not attempt to deprive others of theirs, or impede their efforts to obtain it. Each is the proper guardian of his own health, whether bodily, or mental and spiritual. Mankind are greater gainers by suffering each other to live as seems good to themselves, than by compelling each to live as seems good to the rest.

- Do you agree with Mill's concern and warning that there is a perennial tendency to "strengthen society and diminish the power of the individual"? Provide examples from our current culture to support your response.

- Explain what Mill means in the following passage. Do you agree? Why or why not?

    He who lets the world, or his own portion of it, choose his plan of life for him, has no need of any other faculty than the ape-like one of imitation. He who chooses his plan for himself, employs all his faculties. He must use observation to see, reasoning and judgment to foresee, activity to gather materials for decision, discrimination to decide, and when he has decided, firmness and self-control to hold to his deliberate decision.

- John Rawls, whose ideas we encountered earlier in this chapter, articulates the following criticism of a utilitarian approach to social justice. Evaluate his argument.

    Justice is the first virtue of social institutions, as truth is of systems of thought. A theory however elegant and economical must be rejected or revised if it is untrue; likewise laws and institutions no matter how efficient and well-arranged must be reformed or abolished if they are unjust. Each person possesses an inviolability founded on justice that even the welfare of society as a whole cannot override. For this reason justice denies that the loss of freedom for some is made right by a greater good shared by others. It does not allow that the sacrifices imposed on a few are outweighed by the larger sum of advantages enjoyed by many. Therefore in a just society the liberties of equal citizenship are taken as settled; the rights secured by justice are not subject to political bargaining or to the calculus of social interests. The only thing that permits us to acquiesce in an erroneous theory is the lack of a better one; analogously, an injustice is tolerable only when it is necessary to avoid an even greater injustice. Being first virtues of human activities, truth and justice are uncompromising.